Max
and the
Fake Blood

Max went to the joke shop.

He wanted to play a joke on his dad.

But he didn't know what to buy.

Then Max saw a big bottle of fake blood.

"I will buy this," Max said. "This is just what I need to play a joke on my dad!"

Max went to his room.

He shut the door.

Then he opened the bottle of fake blood.

"This will be the best joke *ever!*" he laughed.

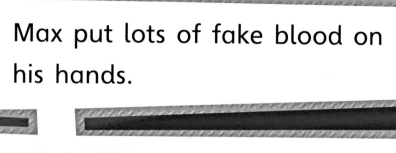

Max put lots of fake blood on his hands.

"Dad will get a big shock when he sees all this blood!" laughed Max.

Max ran into the sitting room.

"Dad! Dad!" he shouted.
"I've cut my hands! I've lost
a lot of blood!"

Dad saw all the blood on Max's hands.
He didn't like the look of all the blood!

8

"Quick, Mum!" Dad shouted.
"Phone for the doctor! Max has
cut his hands. He has lost a lot
of blood!"

Mum phoned the doctor.
"Quick," Mum said,
"I need a doctor!"

"No! No!" said Max. "I don't need a doctor. This blood isn't real. It's fake blood. It's just a joke!"

"*I* know it's fake blood," said Mum. "But Dad thinks it is real! He has had a big shock. The doctor isn't for you. The doctor is for Dad!"

Quiz

Text Detective

- Why did Max's dad faint?
- Do you think it was a good joke to play on Max's dad?

Word Detective

- Phonic Focus: Final consonant clusters
  Page 5: Sound out the four phonemes in 'best'.
  Can you blend the two sounds at the end?
- Page 4: Find a word meaning 'not real'.
- Page 12: Why is the word 'I' in bold print?

Super Speller

Read these words:

best   ever   isn't

Now try to spell them!

HA! HA! HA!

Q Where does a vampire keep his money?

A In a blood bank!

13

Before Reading

Find out about

- How many different types and colours of blood there are

Tricky words

- litres
- blood
- heart
- human
- different
- types
- doctors
- vampires

Introduce these tricky words and help the reader when they come across them later!

Text starter

Did you know you have three litres of blood inside you? The blood in your body keeps you alive and well. Your heart pumps the blood around your body.

Blood!

You have three litres of blood inside you.

You need all this blood to keep you alive and well.

You need a heart to pump the blood round inside you.
The heart pumps the blood round you 40 million times a year!

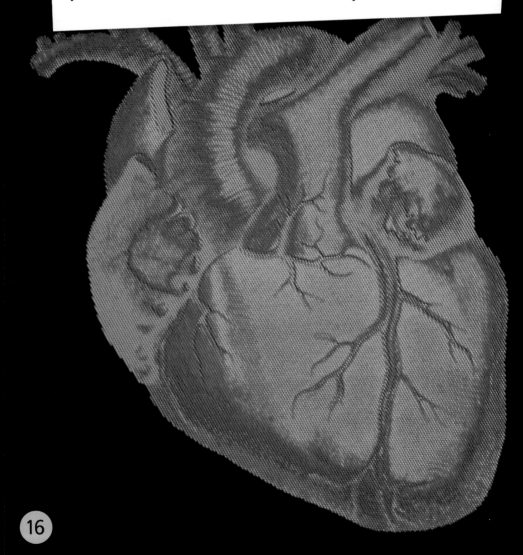

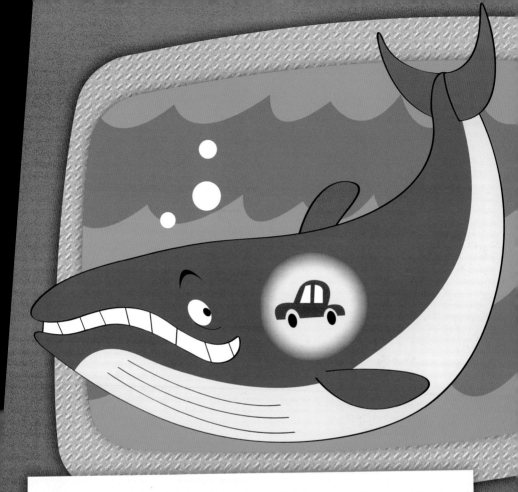

A human heart is as big as a fist.

But a blue whale's heart is as big as a small car!

An earthworm has ten hearts!

Human blood is red.
Most animals have red blood too.

But ...
Some animals have green blood.
Some animals have yellow blood.
Some crabs have blue blood!

horseshoe crab

Some animals have no blood at all!
Jellyfish and flatworms have no
blood.

There are four different types of human blood.

But cows have 800 different types of blood!

Human blood types are: A, B, AB and O.

If you lose lots of blood, doctors can give you more blood.

But they need to know what blood type you are.

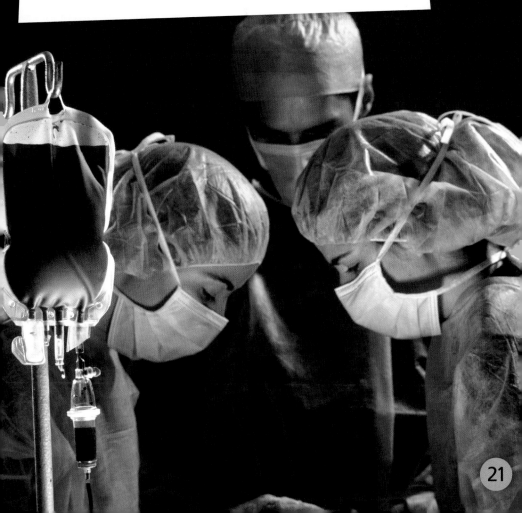

Vampires have to drink human
blood to stay alive.

But vampires are not real!
Vampires are just in films and books.

But vampire bats *are* real!
They have to drink blood to
stay alive.

They drink animal blood but
sometimes they drink human
blood!

Quiz

Text Detective

- What pumps the blood round your body?
- Have you ever seen a vampire in a film?

Word Detective

- **Phonic Focus:** Final consonant clusters
  Page 16: Sound out the four phonemes in 'pump'.
  Can you blend the two sounds at the end?
- Page 17: Can you find two words which are opposite in meaning?
- Page 19: Find two words each made up of two small words.

Super Speller

Read these words:

need   small   four

Now try to spell them!

HA! HA! HA!

Q Why doesn't Dracula have any friends?

A Because he is a pain in the neck!

24